GW00870080

Miserable POeMS

Miserable POEMS

by

ERNEST HENRY

drawings by

DAVIZ

First published in Great Britain in 1999
The Limerick Book Publishing Company, 58 Llanvanor Road, London NW2 2AP

ISBN 1 901 879 80 1

Designed by Silke Klinnert

Printed in Great Britain by
Creative Print and Design (Wales)

To Life And Laughter

ERNEST HENRY

Ernest Henry was born and educated in England. He studied at the Guildhall School of Music and Drama, and started work as a composer, arranger and actor. He appeared in many top television shows including *Doctor Who*, *The Goodies*, *Ripping Yarns*, as well as featuring in many commercials. He moved to Los Angeles in 1978 where he went into television production and syndication. He now lives in London with his wife and two children who inspired his first book, *Poems To Shout Out Loud...*, published by *Bloomsbury* in 1996. This was followed by *Not More Poems to Shout Out Loud* and the best selling book of original poetry for children, *New Improved Limericks*. He has now written other books for children, including *The New Adventures of Phil and Lill*, the captivating adventures of two little kittens, produced the music and words for the hilarious audio cartoon version of *New Improved Limericks - LIVE!* – and recorded his audio books for *EMI*.

More Ernest Henry Books, CDs and Tapes

NEW IMPROVED LIMERICKS *(LIMERICK BOOKS)*

POEMS TO SHOUT OUT LOUD *(BLOOMSBURY)*

NOT MORE POEMS TO SHOUT OUT LOUD *(BLOOMSBURY)*

RUB-A-DUB-DUB *(BLOOMSBURY)*

WISHES FOR MY BABY *(ELEMENT)*

THE NEW ADVENTURES OF PHIL & LILL *(LIMERICK BOOKS)*

MORE ADVENTURES OF PHIL & LILL *(LIMERICK BOOKS)*

AUDIO CASSETTES

POEMS TO SHOUT OUT LOUD *(EMI RECORDS)*

RUB-A-DUB-DUB *(EMI RECORDS)*

NEW IMPROVED LIMERICKS LIVE! *(LIMERICK BOOKS)*

CD

BACK OF THE CLASS *(PIG RECORDS)*

Snotties

The world without snotties
  Would be a sad place,

For what would you use
  To wipe the tears from your face.

Snotty Factor

Hilariously Miserable

Miserably Funny

Sorry, It's So Miserable

Seriously Sad

MISERABLE

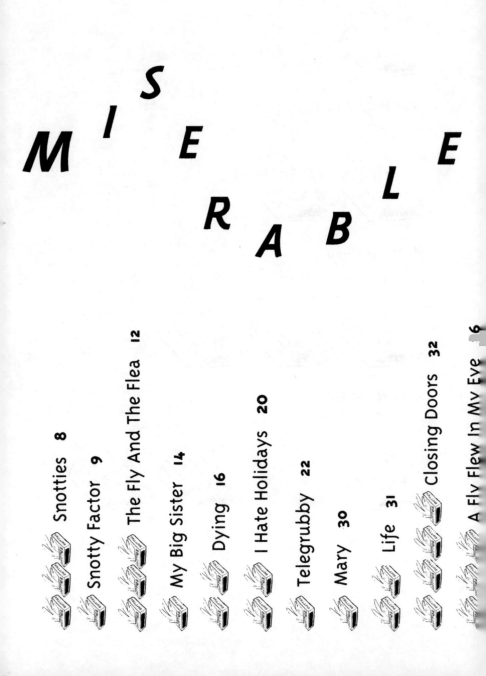

CONTENTS

The Fly
And The Flea

"It seems to me,"

Said the Fly to the Flea,

"That but for two small letters

You could be me."

"It occurs to me,"

Replied the Flea to the Fly

"That if that were an option

I'd rather die."

My Big Sister

My big sister's got a large spot
Right on the end of her nose.
She can't go out with her boyfriends
'Cause her spot's on a spot where it shows.

She tried to cover it with make-up
But all that did was cause a big lump.
I suggested she cut it off with a razor -
All I got for my help was a thump.

I think she should camouflage it,
Or hide it from everyone's gaze
Under a cocktail umbrella:
She might even start a new craze.

My sister's got a real complex
That the spot makes her look like a hag.
So I've simply suggested she places
Her head in a brown paper bag.

Dying

"I'd like to make Arrangements for my burial,"
said the Man,
"I wouldn't want to be a burden on my wife."
"How thoughtful," oozed the Undertaker, rub-
bing sweaty hand,
"One should be well-prepared in death as well
as life."

"Does one have a budget?" he went on and bent
his head
  So he could peer intently through his horn-
rimmed specs.
"We have a simple payment plan to help you
when you're dead:
We take credit cards or cash or even cheques."

"I really hadn't thought about the cost," replied
the Bloke.
"I only need a simple cask in which to rest."
"A simple cask, indeed -" the Unctuous One
began to choke
"Is not what we at Gloom & Son do best."

"A Funeral, dear sir, is an Occasion, an Event.
A time when Pomp and Circumstance come
to a head.
The most important time in Life, and truly
heaven sent,
Is the moment they pronounce that you are
dead."

"Living is everyone," (he never lost a beat!)
"Look around you and you'll see I do not lie.
   People don't look on when you're walking
down the street,
   As they do when your Procession rumbles by."

"A team of valiant horses dressed in plumes of
radiant black,
   Pull your carriage with its cask of shining oak.
   A funeral Ford with a just a coffin chucked
onto the back
   Is not a fitting tribute when you finally croak!"

"So die. Die in Peace, sir, knowing Gloom &
Son will see
   You celebrate your passing in great style.
   The cost, a mere ten thousand pounds, plus the
V.A.T."
The undertaker feigned a weary smile.

"Oh Lord," the Man replied, "I haven't got that
kind of stash.
   I only have three hundred quid here on this
roll."
"Let's have it, then," the Undertaker gruffly
snatched the cash,
"For three hundred we'll just bung you in a
hole!"

I Hate Holidays

I hate holidays
Trooping on the plane
Having baby brothers spilling Coke on me –
again.
Arriving at the hotel where the rooms are double
booked
And listening to Dad complain the way that he's
been crooked.

I hate holidays
Trooping on the beach
Trying to find that perfect
spot which takes an hour to
reach.
Baking in the burning sand
to get all tanned and trim,
And listening to Dad instruct
the world the way to swim.

I hate holidays
Trooping out to eat.
It's half-past nine, I'm famished and have aching
sunburned feet.
Sitting in the restaurant my skin begins to peel,
And listening to Dad instruct them how to cook
his meal.

I hate holidays
Trooping here and there
Seeing sights historical I'd rather be elsewhere:
Sitting in my garden, reading can't be bad,
While Dad bangs on and on about the holiday we
had.

Telegrubby

So there I am –
Had a rotten day at school.
Teacher was rotten.
Lunch was rotten.
Lessons were rotten.
And it's raining.
AND I've got a ton of homework to do.

So I trudge all the way home -
Through the wet, and drag myself up the path to my front door.
I open it - and what do I see?
My little telegrubby rushing up towards me like a whirlwind.

"Ha'o!" he says, beaming, swinging his arms at his side.

"Oh, hello," I reply to the last thing alive on the planet I'd really want to talk to.

"Guess what I've done today?" he says, beaming - again, and swinging those arms of his even higher than he'd done before.

"I dunno," I reply, not really caring, either.

"I had a jam sandwich," Telegrubby explains, seriously, nodding his head now with emphasis, as well as swinging his arms.

"You had a jam sandwich?" I say in disbelief.

I mean, who cares?

"Yes," replies T.G. "I had a jam sandwich. Guess what I did with it?"

Now, what sort of question is that, I thought, and I ask him "Well, what did you do with it, then?"

"I posted it," he replies,
swinging his arms ever more violently now.

"You posted it?"

I can't believe this.

"Yes," Telegrubby continues, earnestly. "I posted my jam sandwich in your video cassette recorder." And he makes a posting movement with his right hand just to prove it.

"It's all gungy and gooey now.   Sorry."

Am I hearing right?

Did this not quite human, relatively small, often pongy alien specimen actually post his crummy tea in my vc.

I advance.

Guns blazing, ready to tear him apart.

"Don't touch me," Telegrubby warns, backing away from me. "Mummy says you can't touch me. *Ugh!*"

And he pokes his tongue out at me!

25

And then it dawns on me that this may not be the only thing my little Telegrotty has been up to today.

So I turn to him, angry, green saliva drooling from the sides of my mouth, gums quivering and bared, with teeth snarling hate as I spit, "What else have you been up to today, you snotty, grotty-tubbie?"

Telegrotty looks back at me angelically.

"Nothing. Nothing, really. Except – you know your Playstation..."

Beads of sweat squeeze through my skin.

I start to shake all over.

My throat is dry.

I croak "No, not my Playstation..." the rest of my sentence is left hanging in mid air, no sound coming from my mouth as my lips form sentences that never can be heard.

"I didn't do anything. I didn't. Honest." Telesnotty looks up, wide-eyed innocence.

"I just looked at it."

I start to relax. But then...

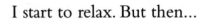

"I took it down from your shelf to see it better," Telegrubby mimes the action he is describing, " 'cause I'm too small. And I put it on the floor. Carefully. At my feet.

" And I looked at it. There. On the floor. By my feet..."

I look at Grotty grubby and start to see worms and maggots oozing from between his hair. His nose flares. His teeth snarl. His eyes blaze with an icy, evil glint.

And he says the mortal words –

"Then I jumped on it – pieces all over the place."

I'm dying.

Why? I think to myself. Why me?

Teleshabby is jumping around, swinging his arms back and forth.

South and North.

I advance - again.

Guns blazing, ready to rid this world (once more) of this demon from hell.

"Don't touch me," he yells, again, backing away. "Mummy says you can't. **Ugh!**" And he pokes his tongue out again and makes a ghastly noise.

"What else have you done, you rotten little ----"

"Nothing," It says. "Really, nothing. Except - you know your CD's?"

I groan.

I'm weak.

I moan "Speak! Tell me the worst."

I grip the chair,

Knuckles white, greying hair.

Drooping, stooping, I don't dare look at the Grottygrubby.

"Well, they were all dirty," he says. "So I put them in the washing-up machine, and they're going round and round and round!"

"Ahhhh!"

Mary

Mary had a little lamb.
She also had a ewe.
Mary loved her little lamb,
Especially in a stew.

Life

Life is never quite
What it seems to be.

What you thought you saw,
Perhaps you didn't see.

And what they said you said,
You surely didn't utter.

Is the butter on the bread?
Or the bread on the butter?

Closing Doors

I shan't see the little House again.
I shan't climb the steep steps up to the front door,
Knock,
And turn the difficult key into
    warmth and fresh baking.

I shan't be able to lunch
    and dose safely snug in the blue velvet chair.
I shan't be able to see the old trees
Each year...
And climb, or see you climb, to reach their fruit.
Or watch you potter about,
Happy...

I shan't be able to feel
    all the mixed emotions in a place I
At once didn't like too much
But called home for so many lives,
And couldn't bear to be away from
And then couldn't bear to return to.

Where you slept...
And I, knowing you were there,
Safe,
Was content,
  at least for that...

For now you've left that place,
  and all this
In mind –
And have gone to somewhere you
  don't know,
  Nor never truly will, as I do.

And we weep,
And hurt, inside and out,
As you should be here with me,
And her:
Us, holding your little head to keep
    the mem'ries in.

But we can't.
Because you need others now
    As much as you need me
Or she:
And we shall, none of us,
Ever see the little House again.

A Fly Flew in My Eye

I can't recount the times
  that I have climbed the greasy pole
The dizzy heights have beckoned
And I reckoned that that my role
In life was set for me to be atop, aloft, on high –
But just as I attained my goal, a fly flew in my eye:

I lost my grip, I fell, I slid to earth with ghastly thud
And ended at the bottom, knee deep in sticky mud.

I can't recount the times
  I've trod the path to ventures new.
The naughty ventures beckoned,
As ventures often do.
They offered bliss, a kiss, a quite substantial piece of pie –
But just as I attained my goal, a fly flew in my eye:

I lost my grip, I fell, I slid to earth with ghastly thud
And ended at the bottom, knee deep in sticky mud.

I tried my hand at cards
  and played the roulette wheel.
I've gambled on the horses. Oh what a thrill
To see the nag you backed a thousand quid on flashing
by...
But just as he attained the post a fly flew in his eye.

I lost my grip, I fell, I slid to earth with ghastly thud
And ended at the bottom, knee deep in sticky mud.

I've once or twice been tempted
  to tie the nuptial knot.
I've picked the spouse I fancied
And bought the family plot.
I'm not a wilting flower or particularly shy
But when she took her wig and makeup off – that fly flew
in my eye.

I lost my grip, I fell, I slid to earth with ghastly thud
And ended at the bottom, knee deep in sticky mud.

My Dad's boring

Every day
He gets up
And goes to work,
And comes home in the evening - tired,
And washes his hands,
And has a drink,
And watches the tele,
And goes to bed.

At weekends
He pays the bills
And does the shopping (with Mum!)
And tries to fix things (not!)
And mows the lawn (when Mum insists!)
And joins us for meals,
And reads the paper.

My Dad's boring:
I'll be like him one day.

It's so unfair!!

The Cheque

"The cheque will be ready
Wednesday,
Thursday,"
The company's director said.
So Thursday came by
And quite naturall-y
I reminded him of what he had said.

"Good God," said the company's director
Shock horror all over his face.
"It's because we have
Procedures
And systems,
And paper all over the place.

"Sign-offs are needed on
Contracts,
Memos,"
The director tried to explain.
"But don't worry, we'll pay you
Tuesday,
Wednesday.
Come back and see me again."

So I went back to see him
Wednesday
Morning,
But the company's director
was out.
His secret'ry said
"Come back later instead,
He'll be here by four, no
doubt."

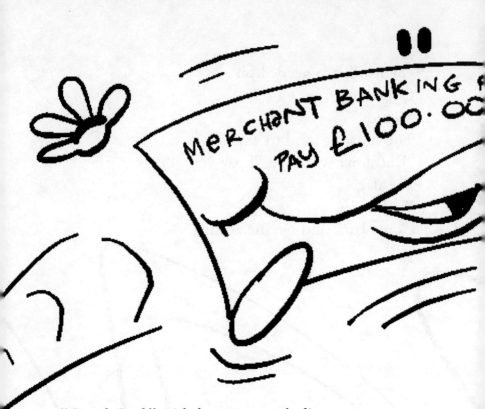

"Good God," said the company's director
When I turned up at four on the dot.
"We had your cheque ready this morning.
Where were you, you silly clot?"

    "I was here in you office,"
I whimpered,
Simpered.
    "I came in at half past eight."
    "Ah," said the company's director,
    "That was far too late."

And with that he pressed his
Buzzer,
Loudly,
Demanding secretarial assist.
"Where's that cheque for our friend
Have you got it?"
She said she'd consult her list:

"It was drawn yesterday
Morning
Early,
And signed there is no doubt.
Accounts have it locked in the safe now:
We can't have cheques laying about."

"Of course not," the company's
Director
Nodded
Solemn with earnest import.
"The safe won't be open till morning:
Come back tomorrow, old sport."

From six in the morning I
Waited
Hated
As I watched every worker
file by.
At nine I asked for the
director
And was told of the
traged–y.

"He passed away only this
Morning
Early.
He died in his sleep, he did."
"Oh dear," I said, "how awful,
He owed me fifty quid.

"Do you think I could have my cheque
now,"
I inquired scratching my head.
"No - the cheque needs to be signed-off,
And the company director's dead.

"But come back next
Wednesday,
Thursday,"
The new director said.
So Thursday came by
And quite naturall-y
The new director was dead.

You Knew Enough

You knew enough to wave goodbye -
And what was that look behind your eye?
Have you forgotten, or do you know why
You're where you are... where you are?

You knew enough to touch my cheek,
To stroke my face, and though quite weak
You smiled, and wanly tried to speak
Of where you are... where you are.

You knew enough to tell me 'go!'
To shut me up and leave you, so
That gentle sleep could ebb and flow
From where you are... to where you are.

I shan't forget your look when I
Touched your arm and heard you sigh.
You knew enough to wave goodbye
To where you are... where you are.

PAUSE

The Cough

I went into the chemist shop
And bought myself a cough.
I could have bought a mixture
But one was quite enough.

NASTY COUGH

CHESTY COUGH

I used it every day,
Every time I took a breath.
It became such a habit -
I coughed myself to death.

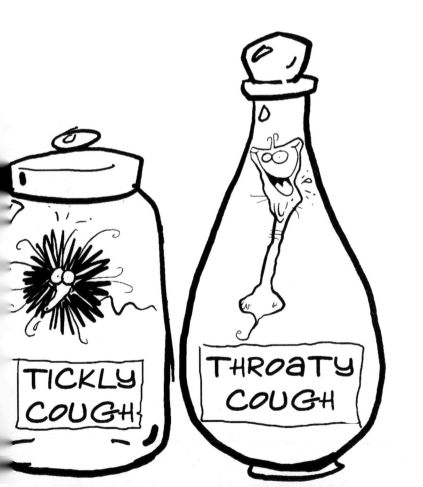

TICKLY COUGH

THROATY COUGH

I Hate Travelling

I always feel sick in a car.
I always feel sick in a plane.
The motion in ships
Ensures that my lips
Meet the food that I ate once again.

The Train

So there you are –
Sitting on the train
With the rain pelting down on the train's window
pane.
And your shoes are all wet
And the carriage is hot
And you're tired and you're hungry and you like
it "not a lot!"

The wheelie-thing comes
Trundling down the isle
Pushed by a sweaty bloke who's trying hard to
smile.
And you ask for a coke
But he's just sold out:
He offers you a coffee but you'd rather do with-
out.

Things look bad.
The carriage starts to smell
Of soggy coats and rancid goats and bacon-
burger hell.
Could it get worse?
It does by an ace
When a beaming baby's head bobs up in front
of your face.

There he is –
Leaning over his seat,
Dribbling down his chin as he waves a sticky
sweet
Which he drops on your lap
And the baby starts to cry
And everyone around you is wondering why!?!?

Accusing eyes
Burn through your head.
Your Mum is so embarrassed that she wishes
she were dead.
You get a clip 'round the ear
And you're grounded for a week,
And another clip around the nut each time
you try and speak!

There he is –
A glint in his eye.
Nasty looking object – you'd like to make
him cry!
And then you see a slimy string
Of snot run down his chin
As he leans towards your Mum with an evil
looking grin.

"Mum!" you warn.
"Are you speaking to me?"
She snarls through her teeth while
sipping Virgin tea.

"Mum, you ought to know..."
And you point towards the brat,
But she refuses to listen –
Mum can be such a prat!

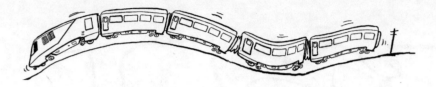

"OK!" you say
And shrug "You'll see!"
And watch while the baby's snot drops in her tea
Which Mum sips blissfully
Unaware,
Finishing the lot before plumping up her hair.

Next stop's yours –
You collect your things and stand
In a queue, in the isle with too much in each hand,
So when the train finally lurches
To a shuddering stop
You're scrambling for all the things the train has made
you drop.

People don't help
As you ferret on the floor:
They want to get off – they've seen it all before
And just as you've got it all
Together once again
You see your station gliding by while you're still stuck
on the train!

So there you are –
Sitting on the train...

My little Brother

My little brother plays the violin -
    and screeches away at it for hours and
hours and hours -
    he's says he's playing bark or somethin'
    but it sounds more like fingernails being
scratched down a blackboard.

When he plays
    the budgie hangs upside down in his
cage... drooling,
    the cat buries itself underneath piles of
cushions
    and the dog laughs hysterically, eyes pop-
ping out of his head, fur all stickin' up.

When he plays
    Dad goes to the pub
and I stuff my ears with
tons of cotton wool.

But Mum – Mum just sits there –
    quietly,
    right next to my little brother.
I mean RIGHT NEXT TO HIM!!!

        Sitting
        Knitting.
        Smiling.
        Quietly listening

        To HIM!!!

Looking lovingly up at her little virtual-oso
(well that's what she calls 'im, anyway.)

When I play my CD, Mum just yells at me
to turn it down!

I mean. It's music, too.

Piggy

I don't know why this book's so sad,
I've laughed so much I'm achin'.
I'm losing weight, can't eat or sleep,
I'm off me eggs an' bacon.

Daviz draws me on my back
An' that's how I'll remain
Until the next book Henry writes
Is in the shops again.

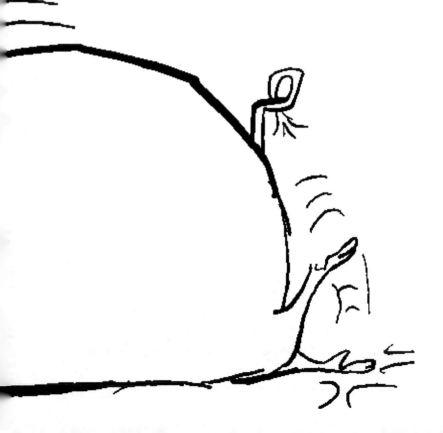

Soulless Night

Let's pray for the little ones – far
and wide
Who cannot rest, who have to
hide;
Who dare not dream for fear they
might
Be taken by a soulless night.

Who have no warmth, no home,
no soap;
Who live in shadows and little
hope
That one day they might live in
light
And not succumb to a soulless
night.

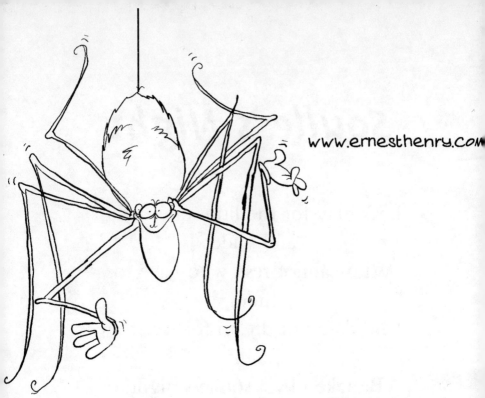

www.ernesthenry.com

Visit these exciting websites and
meet more crazy characters from
the hilarious books by Ernest
Henry and Daviz.

http://daviz.future.easyspace.com/